SCHOLAR Study Guide

CfE Advanced Hig... ....gy
Unit 3: Investigative Biology

Authored by:

Bryony Smith (North Berwick High School)

Dawn Campbell (Falkirk High School)

Reviewed by:

Fiona Stewart (Perth Grammar School)

Previously authored by:

Jaquie Burt

Lorraine Knight

Eileen Humphrey

Nadine Randle

Heriot-Watt University

Edinburgh EH14 4AS, United Kingdom.

Distributed by the SCHOLAR Forum.

SCHOLAR Study Guide Unit 3: CfE Advanced Higher Biology

1. CfE Advanced Higher Biology Course Code: C707 77

ISBN 978-1-909633-62-9

Print Production and fulfilment in UK by Print Trail www.printtrail.com

Acknowledgements

Thanks are due to the members of Heriot-Watt University's SCHOLAR team who planned and created these materials, and to the many colleagues who reviewed the content.

We would like to acknowledge the assistance of the education authorities, colleges, teachers and students who contributed to the SCHOLAR programme and who evaluated these materials.

Grateful acknowledgement is made for permission to use the following material in the SCHOLAR programme:

The Scottish Qualifications Authority for permission to use Past Papers assessments.

The Scottish Government for financial support.

The content of this Study Guide is aligned to the Scottish Qualifications Authority (SQA) curriculum.

Contents

1 Scientific principles and process **1**
   1.1   Scientific method 3
   1.2   Scientific communication and literature 6
   1.3   Scientific ethics 8
   1.4   Learning points 11
   1.5   End of topic test 12

2 Experimentation **15**
   2.1   Pilot studies 17
   2.2   Variables 21
   2.3   Experimental design 24
   2.4   Controls 28
   2.5   Sampling 30
   2.6   Ensuring reliability 33
   2.7   Extended response 36
   2.8   Learning points 37
   2.9   End of topic test 40

3 Critical evaluation of biological research **43**
   3.1   Evaluating background information 45
   3.2   Evaluating experimental design 46
   3.3   Evaluating data analysis 47
   3.4   Evaluating conclusions 51
   3.5   Learning points 55
   3.6   End of topic test 57

4 End of unit test **59**
   4.1   End of Unit 3 test 60

Glossary **66**

Answers to questions and activities **68**
   1   Scientific principles and process 68
   2   Experimentation 70
   3   Critical evaluation of biological research 72
   4   End of unit test 75

Topic 1

Scientific principles and process

Contents

1.1   Scientific method   3
      1.1.1   Scientific cycle model   3
      1.1.2   Null hypothesis and independent verification   5
1.2   Scientific communication and literature   6
1.3   Scientific ethics   8
1.4   Learning points 11
1.5   End of topic test 12

Prerequisite knowledge

You should already know that:

- *scientific reports are written in standard format;*

- *experiments should be repeated for reliability;*

- *experiments should cause no harm or distress to living things or the environment;*

- *risk assessments should be written and followed when carrying out experiments.*

Learning objectives

By the end of this topic you should be able to:

- *describe the scientific cycle, naming the four key parts;*

- *state that in science, ideas, theories and hypotheses are constantly being refined;*

- *define the term null hypothesis;*

- *explain that independent verification is necessary when accepting new scientific concepts;*

- *state that negative results can be important, using medical advances as an example;*

- *state that experiments and findings must be communicated in a standard format that allows repetition by other scientists;*

- *state that experimentation and findings will be subject to peer review and critical evaluation;*

- *explain that where the wider media will provide further critical evaluation, and be able to identify where such critical evaluation is inaccurate or biased;*

- *explain the importance of scientific ethics in terms of unbiased reporting, reliable references and avoiding plagiarism;*

- *state that animals should only be used when absolutely necessary and any harm to them minimal;*

- *explain the ethics involved when working with humans, in terms of consent and the right to withdraw from the study at any time;*

- *describe the influence of risk assessments, legislation, regulation, policy and funding in scientific research.*

1.1   Scientific method

Science is the gathering and organisation of testable and reproducible knowledge. In the scientific cycle there are four key parts:

- hypothesising, questioning and debating a particular idea or area of science;
- investigating through observing, researching or experimenting;
- analysis of data and results from experiments through comparing, interpreting or applying statistics;
- evaluation of results and conclusions are formed.

Based on analysis and evaluations, a new or refined hypothesis may be offered and so the cycle continues (see diagram below).

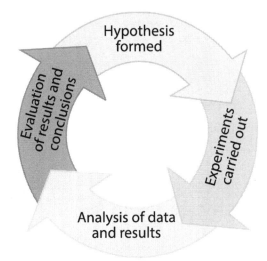

The scientific cycle

1.1.1   Scientific cycle model

In science, ideas, models and theories are constantly being refined. At any one time the current theory is considered to be the best explanation or answer to a hypothesis. After further experimentation, analysis and evaluation an updated theory or model may be offered, thus superseding the previous theory.

Reaching the current fluid mosaic model of the plasma membrane illustrates the scientific cycle perfectly.

The evolution of plasma membrane models

Work on the plasma membrane theory started in 1895, when Charles Overton proposed that lipids were the main components of membranes. He had observed lipid soluble substances enter cells much more quickly than lipid insoluble substances. Of course in 1895, it was still 50 years prior to membranes being viewed with an electron microscope. Twenty years later the idea of proteins also being part of the membrane was introduced.

In 1917, Irving Langmuir introduced the idea that the lipids may in fact be phospholipids, with hydrophilic heads during his work with artificial membranes. Eight years later, two Dutch scientists, E. Gorter and F. Grendel, put forward the hypothesis that cell membranes were phospholipid bilayers, thus explaining how the hydrophobic tails could avoid contact with water. Gorter and Grendel carried out measurements using red blood cells, finding that the phospholipid content to be double that of the surface area of the cells, permitting a double layer. It was discovered later that these two Dutch scientists had miscalculated both the surface area of the cell and the phospholipid quantity, however, the two mistakes cancelled each other out. Their conclusion was correct, but based on erroneous data.

In 1935, Hugh Davson and James Danielli started hypothesising the arrangement of the proteins. They postulated that the phospholipid bilayer was sandwiched between two layers of globular protein. This model seemed to be supported with the introduction of electron microscopy to the study cells in the 1950s. By the 1960s, the Davson-Daneilli sandwich theory was the favoured plasma membrane and organelle membrane model. However, by the end of the 1960s, many cell biologists were noticing two issues with the model:

1. First, not all membranes were identical under the electron microscope. The plasma membrane is 7-8 nm thick with a three-layered structure. Conversely, the mitochondrial inner membrane measures only 6 nm in thickness. The protein content of mitochondrial membranes is greater than that of plasma membranes. Furthermore, the type of phospholipids present was found to differ between different membranes.

2. The second issue with the sandwich model was explaining the protein arrangement. In the sandwich model, the proteins were hypothesised to provide a layer on the membrane surface. This would pose a problem for the sections of the proteins that are hydrophobic. In 1972, a new hypothesis solving this problem was proposed by S. J. Singer and G. Nicolson. Their model saw the proteins scattered and inserted into the phospholipid bilayer. This is the theory we currently accept, the **fluid mosaic model**.

As can be seen, the theory of the plasma membrane was nearly 80 years in the making. This is not unusual in science. Other examples of the scientific cycle are:

- research on DNA structure;
- discovery of plant hormones;
- evidence that genes specify proteins;
- Gregor Mendel's approach to genetics;
- research to identify model organisms for scientific study.

Scientific cycle

Q1: Put the following steps in the scientific cycle into the correct order:

Go online

- Analysing data through comparing, interpreting and applying statistics
- Debating ideas and coming up a hypothesis to test
- Designing appropriate experiments
- Evaluating results
- Forming conclusions
- Observing and collecting data from experiments
- Refining the original hypothesis
- Researching others' work

. . . .

1.1.2   Null hypothesis and independent verification

Can negative results be positive?

Failure to find an effect (i.e. a negative result) is a valid finding, as long as an experiment is well designed. Even conflicting data or conclusions can be resolved through careful analysis and evaluation. Where a resolution cannot be reached, additional and often more creative experimentation can be carried out. In medicine and pharmaceuticals, reporting of negative results is essential in the pursuit of cures for degenerative and acute diseases.

The null hypothesis

The null hypothesis is a hypothesis based on the default position, thus that two variables are unrelated. An example would be 'all daisies have the same number of petals'. Clearly this theory can be easily disproved through discovery of two daisies with a different number of petals. Often scientists will state a null hypothesis and set out to falsify it.

Hypothesis: Larger males are more likely to be selected by a mate.

Null hypothesis: Larger males are not more likely to be selected by a mate.

Should a relationship between larger males and selection be observed through experimentation, the null hypothesis could easily be rejected. Rather than setting out to prove hypotheses, scientists often set out to disprove or falsify null hypotheses.

Independent verification

Scientific ideas only become accepted once they have been verified (or alternatives falsified) independently; one-off results are treated with caution, which is why it is essential to do complete independent repeats of an experiment. Repetition should be done at a different time with a completely new set of ingredients, organisms and chemicals.

Go online

An investigation into whether athletes' body clocks affect competition performance

In this investigation male and female athletes from different sports were used to ascertain whether body clock affected competition performance. It has long been known that some individuals are naturally early risers and others more night owls.

Different athletes train at different times of the day, with a number of factors from work and family life to accessing equipment being amongst the influencing factors. Athletes have little say over timing of competitions though, with these being governed by facilities and often television rights. Early rising female lacrosse players have been shown to have a peak performance at noon, whereas late risers didn't peak until around 8.00 p.m. (Parker et al, 2009).

Obviously in a team sport, it is difficult to suit all players. Clearly, if the findings of the female lacrosse players are found in other sports too, and in both males and females, then this could be highly significant. In some sports, such as sprinting, the margin between a medal or not could come down to hundredths of a second.

Q2: What was the aim of this investigation?

....

Q3: What was the null hypothesis of this investigation?

....

Q4: If the result is a negative result, who might benefit from this being reported and why?

....

1.2   Scientific communication and literature

Scientific reports follow a basic format:

- title;
- aims and hypotheses;
- methods;
- results;
- analysis of results;
- discussion and evaluation.

Scientific reports should be written in a manner that allows other scientists to repeat the experiment for verification or further work.

Scientific findings may be communicated via a range of different means. Scientists from a range of fields may share a selection of findings at conferences and seminars via lectures, talks and poster displays. Furthermore, where findings have been subject to peer review, they may be reported via scientific journals, thus following the common scientific report format.

Review articles

Where a number of scientific findings have been made in a particular field, most scientific journals will publish a review article which sums up the work and findings carried out. These review articles are usually written by experts who are well respected experts in their chosen area of scientific research.

Referencing

When referencing:

- cite and reference these in a standard format;
- use only references that are reliable and unbiased;
- care must be taken to avoid **plagiarism**.

Plagiarism can be avoided by putting statements into your own words and clearly citing sources. Never include large chunks of copied material or long quotations.

Referencing - standard format

- **Books**

  Author(s) (surname followed by initials). (Year). Book title. Place: Publisher.

  Example reference: Raven, P.H., Evert, R. F. and Eichhorn, S. E. (1999). Biology of Plants (6ed). New York: W. H. Freeman and Company.

- **Journal articles**

  Author(s) (surname followed by initials). (Year). Article title. Journal Title Volume (issue), pages.

  Example reference: Tanner, K. (2012). Promoting Student Metacognition. Life Science Education 11, 113-120.

- **Web page**

  Author. (Year). Title. Available at: web address of document [Accessed: Day Month Year].

  Example reference: Robins, C. (2015). Athletes Vs Non-Athletes Heart Rate. Available at: http://www.livestrong.com/article/82658-athletes-vs.-nonathletes-heart-rate/ [Accessed: 15/12/15]

If there is no clear author, the organisation should replace the author.

If there is no date, state (no date) instead.

1.3 Scientific ethics

Integrity and honesty

All findings must be presented in an unbiased manner. Other scientists may of course dispute or disagree with findings; however, trust in findings is increased through referencing others' findings.

Peer review

Scientists who specialise in a particular field read reports prior to publication, assessing reliability. These specialists may advise the writer to make changes to enhance the scientific rigour of the piece before it can be published. Once the article is finally published, scrutiny of the findings continues through further critical evaluation via coverage in the wider media. It is vital that this scientific information is presented to the wider media in an unbiased and understandable manner.

Increasing the public understanding of science and the issue of misrepresentation of science in the media can be difficult. Sometimes members of the public do not feel they can access the information due to the technical terms and jargon used. With current topical science surrounding stem cell research, genetic engineering, DNA technology, food security and pharmacology it is even more important to present the information in an unbiased and accessible manner to allow the public to make well-formed opinions.

Too often, the media has created panic regarding scientific matters that have adversely affected individuals. One example is that of the controversy surrounding the MMR vaccination in the late 1990s. Parents were put in a very difficult position about whether to have their children vaccinated against these serious diseases when an article was published in 1998 by Andrew Wakefield based on a very small sample size, with ambiguous results suggesting that there might be a link between MMR and autism. Wakefield's publications included a review paper with no new evidence, published in a minor journal, and two papers on laboratory work where he provided data that the measles virus had been found in tissue samples taken from children who had autism and bowel problems.

Wide media coverage followed, with very emotive stories from distressed parents. The health service came under attack and controversy grew further when the Prime Minister at the time refused to say whether his young son had been immunized or not. In very recent years, outbreaks of these diseases have been reported in unvaccinated teenagers. Mumps, as an example, is particularly dangerous to teenage boys who may suffer infertility as a result of the disease. Although this study has now been completely discredited, some of the general public still believe these findings. This is a clear example of the consequences of poor science that has caused significant harm to children.

Replication of experiments by peers also reduces the opportunity for dishonesty or any deliberate misuse of science.

Animal studies

Using animals in studies is often unavoidable, but does lead to advances in medicine. Where the use of animals is unavoidable, the 3Rs are recommended:

1. *Replacement* - can the animal be replaced with another? Who decides which animals are acceptable for use and which are not though?

2. *Reduction* - can fewer animals be used?

3. *Refinement* - can the procedure be refined to reduce human error?

It is essential that scientists use models or alternatives to animals where possible. However, should using an animal be unavoidable this must be well documented. Any experiments involving animals are strictly controlled, requiring licensed premises and licenses to carry out each piece of research. Researchers must provide full justification of which animals are to be used and why. They must also state the expected positive impact on humans and society that using these animals will bring.

Human studies

In any studies involving humans, informed consent should always be sought. If participants are under 16, a parent or carer must also provide informed consent. Participants must be aware of the right to withdraw data at any time during the investigation. Participant confidentiality must be maintained too.

Through providing informed consent, participants will be able to assess if their participation may contribute to findings that could impact on society or the environment.

Justification

All scientific investigations must be justifiable, thus clearly have benefits to society or the environment, or merely the pursuit of scientific knowledge.

Scientific investigations are influenced by:

1. risk assessments that must take account of that safety of humans or animals involved and any impact on the environment;

2. regulation, policy and licensing by governments which aim to limit the potential for the misuse of studies and data;

3. funding which can influence the direction and pace of scientific progress.

Scientific ethics

Q5: Match up the correct term about using animals in scientific studies with its definition.

Go online

- Replace;
- Reduce;
- Refine.

Term	Definition
	Ensuring competence in the experimental technique to reduce human error.
	Using a different type of animal in the study.
	Using fewer animals in the study.

....

Go online

An investigation into whether athletes' body clocks affect competition performance

It has long been known that some individuals are naturally early risers and others more night owls. Different athletes train at different times of the day, with a number of factors from work and family life to accessing equipment being amongst the influencing factors. Athletes have little say over timing of competitions though, with these being governed by facilities and often television rights. Early rising female lacrosse players have been shown to have a peak performance at noon, whereas late risers didn't peak until around 8.00 p.m. (Parker et al, 2009).

Obviously in a team sport, it is difficult to suit all players. Clearly, though, these findings, if shown in other events and in both males and females, could be highly significant. In some sports, such as sprinting, the margin between a medal or not could come down to hundredths of a second.

A professor of Sports Science wanted to further research whether an athlete's body clock had an impact on what time of day they would perform better in a competition.

Three groups of 20 athletes (10 male and 10 female) from a range of sports were used:

- Group 1 - athletes that were 'morning people' (early morning risers);

- Group 2 - athletes that were 'night owls' (late morning risers);

- Group 3 - athletes that had no preference to getting up late or early.

Q6: Describe any ethical considerations that should have been part of the design of this investigation.

....

Q7: In the background information, the author states: "Early rising female lacrosse players have been shown to have a peak performance at noon, whereas late risers didn't peak until around 8.00 p.m."

How is this statement justified by the author?

....

1.4 Learning points

Summary

- Scientific cycle involves setting testable hypotheses or null hypotheses, followed by suitable experimentation and subsequent data collection. Data should then be analysed and results evaluated. Conclusions can then be drawn and hypotheses modified accordingly. These modified hypotheses can then be tested and so the cycle continues.

- Null hypotheses are hypotheses stating that one variable will have no effect on the other.

- Scientific ideas require independent verification before being published and supported by similar findings in a number of other investigations before being accepted.

- Scientific findings and investigations must be reported in the standard format, with enough detail to be repeated by other scientists.

- All findings are subject to critical evaluation from peers, in peer review and by the public through the wider media.

- When reporting findings, this must be done in an unbiased manner, backed by reliable sources, referenced in the standard format.

- Plagiarism must be avoided.

- When using animals, harm should be minimised and scientists should consider replacement, reduction and refinement.

- When using humans, consent is essential and subjects must be aware of their right to withdraw their data at any time.

- Confidentiality must be provided to human subjects.

- Scientific investigations must follow a working risk assessment.

- Legislation, regulation, policy and funding can all influence scientific research.

1.5   End of topic test

End of Topic 1 test

Go online

Q8: A scientist predicts that the speed of cycling will have no effect on the oxygen consumption of cyclists. What term is used to describe this statement? *(1 mark)*

. . . .

Q9: Before publication of a scientific article, others scientists read the article and make any comments or suggestions to the author prior to publication. What is this process called? *(1 mark)*

. . . .

Q10: Which of the following statements about results are true: *(4 marks)*

a) Results can be negative.

b) Results can be positive.

c) Results will be verified by a friend.

d) Results will be verified independently.

e) One-off results are easily accepted.

f) Results may cause a hypothesis to be rejected.

. . . .

Q11: Complete the following sentence about scientific literature and communication.

Scientific reports should be written in a manner that allows other scientists to . . . . the experiment for verification or further work. *(1 mark)*

. . . .

Q12: Referencing: *(1 mark)*

a) can reduce bias.

b) has a standard format.

c) is plagiarising others' work.

. . . .

Q13: Identify the 3 'R's of using animals in scientific studies. *(1 mark)*

a) Reduce, reuse and replace

b) Reduce, replace and refine

c) Reuse, repeat and replace

d) Random, refine and reduce

. . . .

Q14: Which of the following statements about using humans in studies are correct? *(2 marks)*

a) Consent is only required for children.

b) Consent is only required for adults.

c) Consent is required for all.

d) Subjects can withdraw data at any time.

e) Subjects can only withdraw data until the halfway point.

f) Subjects can never withdraw their data.

. . . .

Topic 2

Experimentation

Contents

2.1   Pilot studies   17
    2.1.1   Pilot study examples   18
2.2   Variables   21
    2.2.1   Independent, dependent and confounding variables   21
    2.2.2   Discrete and continuous variables   22
    2.2.3   Qualitative, quantitative and ranked data   22
2.3   Experimental design   24
    2.3.1   Simple vs. multifactorial experiments   24
    2.3.2   In vitro vs. in vivo experiments   25
    2.3.3   Laboratory experiments vs. field experiments   26
    2.3.4   Observational studies   27
2.4   Controls   28
2.5   Sampling   30
    2.5.1   Random sampling   31
    2.5.2   Systematic sampling   32
    2.5.3   Stratified sampling   32
2.6   Ensuring reliability   33
2.7   Extended response   36
2.8   Learning points   37
2.9   End of topic test   40

Prerequisite knowledge

You should already know that:

- *in an experiment the independent variable is the variable which is manipulated or changed by the investigator and the dependent variable is the variable which is measured;*

- *within an experiment there are certain key variables which must be controlled in order to obtain a valid result;*

- *the results of control groups are used for comparison with treatment results;*

- *experiments are repeated and average results are calculated to improve the reliability of the results.*

Learning objectives

By the end of this topic you should be able to:

- *describe the information which can be gathered from pilot studies;*

- *describe the advantages of performing a pilot study;*

- *explain the term confounding variables and the importance of controlling or monitoring these variables;*

- *describe the use of randomised block design;*

- *state that variables can be discrete or continuous and give rise to qualitative, quantitative or ranked data;*

- *state that the type of variable being investigated has consequences for any graphical display or statistical tests that may be used;*

- *state that the experimental treatment group is compared to a control;*

- *describe the difference between simple and multifactorial experiments;*

- *state that the control of laboratory conditions allows simple experiments to be conducted more easily than in the field;*

- *state that experiments conducted in vivo tend to be more complex than those in vitro;*

- *describe the drawback of simple experiments;*

- *describe the role of observational studies;*

- *describe the use of positive and negative controls;*

- *explain why controls are required in experimental procedure;*

- *state that sampling allows determination of a representative sample of a population;*

- *describe the relationship between variation in a population and sample size;*

- *state that a representative sample should share the same mean and the same degree of variation about the mean as the population as a whole;*

- *describe the processes of random, systematic and stratified sampling;*

- *state that variation in experimental results may be due to the reliability of measurement methods and/or inherent variation in the specimens;*

- *explain how the reliability of measuring instruments or procedures can be determined;*

- *explain how the natural variation in biological material being used can be determined;*

- *state that overall results can only be considered reliable if they can be achieved consistently.*

2.1 Pilot studies

A pilot study is a small-scale investigation of a planned research project. The main aim of a pilot study is to assess validity and check procedures/techniques; this allows evaluation and modification of the experimental design. Pilot studies are also known as 'feasibility' studies since they investigate whether a suggested protocol is feasible, i.e. capable of delivering valid and reliable results.

Pilot studies are becoming integral to the development of any research project due to their ability to flag up potential issues with a main study and therefore prevent costly mistakes, time wasting or even failure of the project as a whole. Conducting a pilot study does not guarantee success of a project but a good pilot study increases the likelihood of success.

A pilot study can be used to develop and/or practice protocols in order to:

- ensure the experimental design is valid;

- check effectiveness of techniques;

- identify and control confounding variables;

- identify a suitable number of replicates required to give a true value for each independent datum point.

Pilot studies allow development of a new protocol as well as enabling the investigator to become proficient in using an established protocol. The use of a pilot study can ensure an appropriate range of values for the independent variable to avoid results for the dependent variable ending up 'off the scale'. A pilot study can also be used to check whether results can be produced in a suitable time frame.

The diagram below details the advantages of conducting a pilot study.

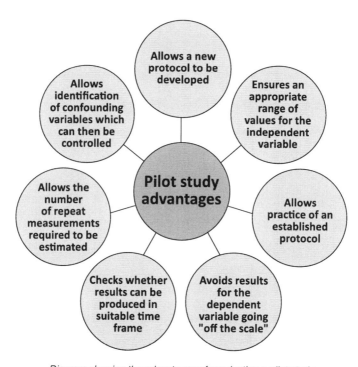

Diagram showing the advantages of conducting a pilot study

2.1.1   Pilot study examples

Example 1

A researcher investigating learning in rats built a maze which included one way doors to prevent the rats from retracing their steps. Before conducting the formal investigation she carried out a pilot study using two rats. Whilst carrying out the pilot study she noticed that the one way doors did not stay open long enough to allow the rats' tails to pass through. The rats learned that going through a door meant their tail would be struck and they began to refuse to enter new sections of the maze. To solve the issue, the researcher placed small wooden blocks at the bottom of the doors to allow the rats' tails to pass through unharmed. As a result of this modification, the rats were not afraid to enter the next section of the maze and the formal investigation was completed without any experimental design flaws.

Laboratory rat
(Source: National Cancer Institute (http://1.usa.gov/1VEl22l))

Example 2

A student was investigating the inhibitory effects of lead on the activity of the enzyme catechol oxidase. The student would be mixing catechol (the substrate) with catechol oxidase and lead ethanoate at varying concentrations, then determining the activity of catechol oxidase. Before beginning the full investigation, the student conducted a pilot study to determine the concentrations of lead ethanoate which should be used in the main study. This allowed the student to ensure she was using an appropriate range of values for the independent variable (lead ethanoate concentration) and avoided the results for the dependent variable going "off the scale" i.e. 100% inhibition.

Example 3

Chromatin immunoprecipitation (ChIP) is a technique which allows researchers to investigate DNA-protein interactions. ChIP is a complex multi-step process (outlined in the diagram below). A researcher performing ChIP for the first time conducted a pilot study to become proficient in the technique before applying it to his area of research.

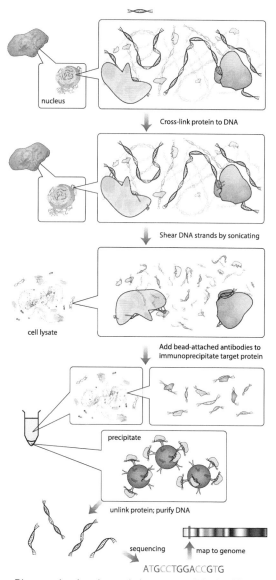

Cross-link protein to DNA

Shear DNA strands by sonicating

Add bead-attached antibodies to immunoprecipitate target protein

unlink protein; purify DNA

sequencing   map to genome

ATGCCTGGACCGTG

Diagram showing chromatin immunoprecipitation (ChIP)
(Chromatin immunoprecipitation sequencing (http://bit.ly/1QxvA2Y) by Jkwchui (htt
p://bit.ly/1NMWMdp) is licensed under CC BY-SA 3.0 (http://bit.ly/1kvyKWi))

2.2 Variables

Any scientific experiment will be subject to a series of variables. Variables are factors which can be changed, controlled or measured within an experiment.

An experiment usually has three types of variables: independent, dependent and confounding.

Variables within a scientific experiment can be discrete or continuous.

Experiments can give rise to qualitative, quantitative and ranked data.

2.2.1 Independent, dependent and confounding variables

The **independent variable** is the variable that is changed or controlled in a scientific experiment to test the effects on the dependent variable. The **dependent variable** is the variable being tested and measured in a scientific experiment.

Daphnia are a type of **plankton** whose heart rate can be directly monitored by observation through a microscope. A student carried out an investigation into the effect of water temperature on heart rate in *Daphnia*. For this experiment, water temperature (°C) is the independent variable and heart rate (beats per minute) is the dependent variable.

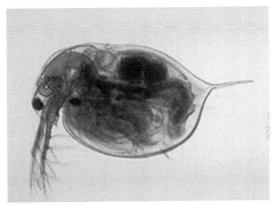

Daphnia
*(Daphnia magna (http://bit.ly/1LbHCb6) by Ayacop (http://bit.ly/1QkdyIF) is
licensed under CC BY 2.5 (http://bit.ly/1em5XTc))*

Due to the complexities of biological systems, other variables besides the independent variable may affect the dependent variable. These variables are known as **confounding variables**. A confounding variable is any factor which affects the dependent variable that is not the independent variable. These confounding variables must be held constant if possible, or at least monitored so that their effect on the results can be accounted for in the analysis.

In the experiment investigating the effect of water temperature on heart rate in *Daphnia* there will be many confounding variables for example age of *Daphnia*, size of *Daphnia*, light intensity of surroundings, pH of water, mineral content of water and method of counting heartbeat.

In cases where confounding variables cannot easily be controlled, blocks of experimental and control groups can be distributed in such a way that the influence of any confounding variable is likely to be the same across the experimental and control groups. In randomised block design experimental subjects are assigned into groups or "blocks" before being assigned to a treatment group. For example size of the *Daphnia* has been identified as a confounding variable in the investigation described above. To carry out a randomized block design, the *Daphnia* would first be placed into groups according to their size. Then from each group, individuals would be assigned to the different temperature treatment groups. In this way the influence of *Daphnia* size is likely to be the same across the experimental and control groups.

2.2.2   Discrete and continuous variables

Variables within a scientific experiment can be *discrete* or *continuous*.

Discrete variables are distinct and unrelated to each other, for example an experiment investigating the effect of different chemicals on *Daphnia* heart rate, the independent variable (the different chemicals) is discrete.

Continuous variables have a range of values for example an experiment investigating the effect of temperature on *Daphnia* heart rate, the independent variable (temperature) is continuous.

The type of variable being investigated has consequences for any graphical display or statistical tests that may be used. For example, experiments where the independent variable is discrete display results using bar graphs whereas experiments with a continuous independent variable display results using line graphs.

2.2.3   Qualitative, quantitative and ranked data

Whether a variable is discrete or continuous, it can give rise to qualitative, quantitative or ranked data.

Quantitative data is information about quantities. In other words it refers to information which can be measured with numbers, e.g. volume, mass, time, temperature etc.

Qualitative data is information about qualities and often involves descriptions. In this case the information can be observed but cannot actually be measured e.g. case studies and interviews.

Some experiments may also give rise to *ranked data*. One form of ranked data places observations into an order from smallest to largest (or vice versa), despite not knowing the exact values. For example a group of researchers observing six male colobus monkeys in a zoo were attempting to determine the dominance hierarchy which existed within the group.

Colobus monkey
(Colobus Monkey at the Oregon Zoo (http://bit.ly/1O5nmwE) by Cacophony (http://
bit.ly/1MDjgwq) is licensed under CC BY-SA 3.0 (http://bit.ly/1kvyKWi))

By observing the pushing behaviour of the monkeys the researchers were able to establish a rank order of dominance amongst the six male monkeys, from most dominant to least dominant. The results are shown in the table below.

Monkey name	Dominance rank
Aldo	1
Bandar	2
Clyde	3
Yono	4
Ari	5
Virgil	6

Ranked data

Another form of ranked data involves sorting data into order and replacing each value with a number to represent its position in the sequence. For example following on from the experiment above to determine the rank order of dominance in the group of male monkeys, researchers wanted to investigate the relationship between **parasite load** and dominance. They counted the number of *Trichuris* worm eggs per gram of faeces in each of the monkeys to determine parasite load. This quantitative data was then converted into ranked data shown in the table below. Using the information in the table, statistical tests can be performed to determine if the two variables (dominance rank and parasite load) covary.

Monkey name	Dominance rank	Egg per gram of faeces	Eggs per gram (rank)
Aldo	1	5678	1
Bandar	2	4333	2
Clyde	3	2836	3
Yono	4	1642	4
Ari	5	793	6
Virgil	6	843	5

Ranked data

2.3 Experimental design

In a scientific experiment, the independent variable is manipulated by the investigator in an attempt to discover an effect on the dependent variable. In order to obtain valid results the experimental design must be sound. Experimental design will need to take into account:

- What variables are being investigated?
- What are the independent and dependent variables?
- What range of values for the independent variable should be used?
- How will the dependent variable be monitored/measured?
- What is a suitable sample size?
- What controls are required?
- What are the confounding variables?
- How can the confounding variables be controlled/monitored?
- How many experimental replicates will be performed?

2.3.1 Simple vs. multifactorial experiments

The difficulty in designing an experiment will vary depending on the type and complexity of the experiment. Simple experiments involve a single independent variable. For example, many enzyme experiments (e.g. investigating the effect of temperature on the activity of the enzyme catalase) are simple experiments. There is only one independent variable and the confounding variables (such as pH, concentration of substrate etc.) can be easily controlled.

A multifactorial experiment involves a combination of more than one independent variable or combination of treatments. This is a more complex type of experiment compared to one which has a single independent variable. This seems to be contrary to what has gone before: how can an experiment have more than one independent variable? Take, for instance, the effect of drugs on human physiology. Many drugs alter their effect when combined with other therapies. While examining the effect of one drug on its own may provide a single independent variable, the results of this study are less useful if the drug is usually used in combination with one or more other therapies. The table below shows the different treatment groups in a multifactorial experiment investigating the effects of an antidepressant drug (Prozac) in combination with a form of psychotherapy called cognitive behavioural therapy (CBT).

		Drug therapy	
		Placebo	Prozac
Psychotherapy	None	Control	Prozac only
	CBT	CBT only	Combined therapy

Multifactorial experiment

At the end of the experiment the severity of depression can be measured (using the Beck Depression Inventory (BDI)) and the results between the different treatment groups can be analysed. In this case conducting a multifactorial experiment provides more robust findings into the benefits of combining psychotherapy and drug therapy in treating depression rather than looking at each factor individually. In general, as experimental designs increase in complexity, more information can be obtained and analysed as well as allowing the detection of interaction effects.

2.3.2 In vitro vs. in vivo experiments

Experiments can be carried out in vitro or in vivo. An in vitro experiment describes an investigation which is carried out using biological molecules or cells out with their normal biological system, e.g. cell culture. An in vivo experiment describes an investigation which is carried out using a living organism, e.g. mouse model organism.

In vitro   *In vivo*

*(Cell Culture in a tiny Petri dish (http://bit.ly/1IID3pY) by kaibara87 (http://bit.ly/1
WOOk37) is licensed under CC BY 2.0 (http://bit.ly/1rRyEZO),
Laboratory mouse (http://bit.ly/1GYpW85) by Rama (http://bit.ly/20OGm9s) is
licensed under CC BY-SA 2.0 FR (http://bit.ly/1LbNXU7))*

An in vitro experiment may be elegant and easily controlled but its relevance may be limited in vivo. In vivo experiments allow researchers to investigate the overall effect of an agent on a living organism. For example in vitro testing using cells in culture may be used as an initial safety test of a new therapeutic compound; however, in vivo testing using an animal model must be performed before advancing to human clinical trials as this will allow the investigators to assess the performance of the drug within a biological system.

2.3.3   Laboratory experiments vs. field experiments

Laboratory experiments are carried out in an artificial and controlled environment, whereas field experiments are conducted in a natural setting. Field studies are the norm for many branches of biology such as psychology and environmental biology. Experiments carried out in a laboratory tend to be more straightforward than those conducted in the field due to the ability of the investigator to easily control the laboratory conditions. Field experiments may provide results which are more applicable to a wider biological setting; however, their drawback lies in the lack of control of experimental variables.

A clinical trial testing the effects of a new medicine is an example of a field experiment. Clinical trials are often conducted as field experiments since it would be impractical to ask subjects to live in a controlled environment for a long period of time. This form of experiment also has the added benefit of allowing the researcher to assess the performance of the medicine while the subjects are going about their normal daily routine; therefore giving more robust results. The main drawback of field experiments is the difficulty in controlling all experimental variables. For example, while participating in the clinical trial, the subjects may be told not to consume alcohol. The researcher cannot guarantee that the subjects will comply with this rule and if anyone fails to comply the results of the trial may be affected.

Plant field trials are another example of a field experiment. The aim of plant breeding is to produce cultivars that will have good yield in the growth conditions typical for that crop. Final crop growth is a result of both genetic and environmental factors. A new plant variety may grow well in a laboratory environment; however, its performance will have to be evaluated in a field trial (field experiment) to provide results which are more applicable to the conditions in which the plant will be grown.

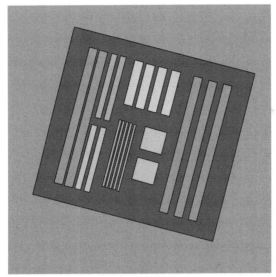

Plant field trials

Each plot in the field shown above can be used to evaluate the growth of a different crop.

2.3.4 Observational studies

Observational studies use groups that already exist to carry out an investigation. For example a study investigating the relationship between smoking and lung cancer would recruit an experimental group of people who have been smoking for 20 years and a control group of people who have never smoked. This is the only viable method to recruit participants to this investigation as it would be unethical to ask a group of individuals to smoke for 20 years to allow a comparison to a control group. Recruiting experimental groups in this way also allows researchers to study long-term effects of certain variables (i.e. effects lasting decades) which may not otherwise be possible.

Because observational studies use groups that already exist, the researcher is not able to tightly control the composition of the experimental groups; this means there is the potential for bias in the groups to affect the results of the study and there is no truly independent variable. As a result, these 'observational' studies are good at detecting correlation but, as they do not directly test the model, they are less useful for determining causation.

In the smoking example mentioned earlier researchers may suggest that there is a correlation between smoking and increased incidence of lung cancer; however, this does not necessarily suggest causation. Before causation can be determined other factors such as diet, genetics and lifestyle of the subjects would need to be analysed.

2.4 Controls

Control experiments are an essential aspect of all valid scientific research projects. The results of control groups can be used to determine if an experiment is working properly at a procedural level and are also used for comparison with treatment results. Experiments usually employ one (or both) of the following types of control:

- positive control;
- negative control.

A positive control is a treatment that is included to check that the system can detect a positive result when it occurs. This group is expected to have a positive result and proves to the researcher that the experimental design being used is capable of producing results.

Imagine an experiment investigating the effect of a newly discovered antibiotic on the growth of *E. coli* bacteria. Petri dishes containing agar and different concentrations of the new antibiotic would be set up alongside a positive control dish containing agar with an antibiotic which is known to inhibit the growth of *E. coli*. A known concentration and volume of *E. coli* bacteria would be spread on the agar surface of each petri dish and incubated for 24 hours. If growth is observed on all the petri dishes, except the positive control, this suggests that the new antibiotic is not capable of inhibiting the growth of *E. coli*. If growth is observed on all the petri dishes, including the positive control, this suggests there is a flaw in the experimental design or procedure. Positive scientific control groups reduce the chances of false negative results.

A negative control group provides results in the absence of a treatment. If a negative control yields an unexpected result this could suggest that there is an unknown confounding variable affecting the experiment and therefore the results would be considered invalid.

In the antibiotic example mentioned earlier, a petri dish containing agar only would be set up to act as a negative control. A known concentration and volume of *E. coli* bacteria would be spread on the agar surface of the petri dish and incubated for 24 hours. If inhibition of growth is observed on all the petri dishes, except the negative control, this suggests that the new antibiotic is capable of inhibiting the growth of *E. coli*. If inhibition of growth is observed on all the petri dishes, including the negative control, this suggests there is another variable affecting the inhibition of growth and the results are invalid. Negative scientific control groups reduce the chances of false positive results.

For each of the following experiments, read the description of each experiment and the controls it included.

Controlled experiment 1

A researcher carried out a clinical trial to investigate the effectiveness of a new medication which controls asthma symptoms. A group of asthmatic subjects were randomly assigned to one of three groups, one experimental group and two control groups. Subjects were told to use a specific inhaler twice a day over a period of six weeks and take a peak flow reading morning and afternoon each day. Peak flow is a measure of the fastest airflow that can be blown from the lungs.

 Go online

Decide if the description of each of the following control groups indicates a positive or negative control.

Q1: In one control group, the subjects were given an inhaler containing a medication which has already proved to be effective in reducing asthma symptoms.

a) Positive
b) Negative

....

Q2: In one control group, the subjects were given an inhaler containing a **placebo**.

a) Positive
b) Negative

....

Controlled experiment 2

A researcher carried out an enzyme assay to determine the quantity of enzyme in an extract. The reaction rate of the enzyme was determined by monitoring the accumulation of the product with time. The quantity of enzyme present was calculated from the observed reaction rate.

 Go online

Decide if the description of each of the following control groups indicates a positive or negative control.

Q3: A control was set up containing no enzyme.

a) Positive
b) Negative

....

Q4: A control was set up containing a known quantity of the purified enzyme.

a) Positive
b) Negative

....

Controlled experiment 3

ELISA is a technique which uses antibodies to detect the presence of a particular protein within a sample solution. ELISA can be used to perform HIV tests on patient samples.

 Go online

A scientist added small volumes of a patient sample to three wells of a multiwell plate. A primary antibody was added to each well followed by a secondary antibody linked to a reporter enzyme (the secondary antibody binds to the primary antibody). A colour-producing substrate was then added and the wells were observed for a colour change. If no colour change is observed this indicates a negative result (no HIV protein present) if a colour change is observed this indicates a positive result (HIV protein present).

Decide if the description of each of the following control groups indicates a positive or negative control.

Q5: For one control, three wells contained a solution with no antigen, along with the primary antibody, secondary antibody and colour-producing substrate.

a) Positive
b) Negative

. . . .

Q6: For one control, three wells contained a solution with a known concentration of the protein of interest, along with the primary antibody, secondary antibody and colour-producing substrate.

a) Positive
b) Negative

. . . .

2.5 Sampling

For many investigations, sampling an entire population (or ecosystem) simply is not feasible. This may be due to lack of money, time constraints, lack of equipment, sheer number of subjects etc. When conducting an investigation, an appropriate sampling strategy must be used. This allows the researcher to select a representative sample of the population and use the results to reach conclusions about the population as a whole.

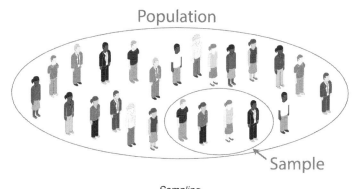

Sampling

A challenge which all researchers face is determining an appropriate sample size for an investigation. A large sample may yield more reliable results; however, correlations can be lost due to "noise" in the data. In general, the extent of the natural variation within a population determines the appropriate sample size. The more variable a population is, the larger the sample size which is required. A representative sample should share the same mean and the same degree of variation about the mean as the population as a whole.

The degree of variation within a population is often determined by calculating standard deviation (SD). Standard deviation is a measure which allows the amount of variation in a set of data to be quantified. In general a larger sample size will yield a standard deviation which is closer to that of the population as a whole. Correspondingly, a larger sample size should also give a more accurate estimation of the population mean. Calculating the true mean or SD of a whole population can also be challenging as it may not be possible to determine the true value for each individual within the main population. Ultimately all researchers must remember that the data gathered from a sample group only represents a subset of the whole population; therefore, any conclusions drawn from the investigation are subject to a margin of error.

To achieve a representative sample group researchers may employ one of three different sampling strategies:

- random sampling;
- systematic sampling;
- stratified sampling.

2.5.1 Random sampling

In random sampling, members of the population have an equal chance of being selected. This reduces the possibility of bias in the sampling group. When sampling a population, the individuals are numbered and selected at random to form the sample group (as shown in the diagram below). When sampling an ecosystem a grid can be drawn over a map of the area of study and random coordinates are selected to determine the location of the sampling points.

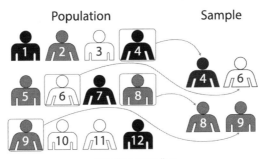

Random sampling

The advantages of random sampling are that it is a straightforward process and avoids bias in the sample group. One disadvantage of random sampling is that it can result in poor representation of the main population/area if certain members/areas are not selected by the random numbers generated. There may also be issues with accessing all the selected members of the population or sites from an area of study.

2.5.2 Systematic sampling

In systematic sampling, members of a population are selected at regular intervals. For example members of a population may be listed and every fourth individual selected to form part of the sample group. In an environmental study, systematic sampling may involve samples being taken in a regular pattern, i.e. every three metres along a transect line.

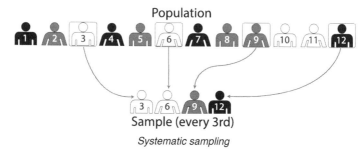

Systematic sampling

The advantage of systematic sampling lies in the fact that it should provide a more representative sample of the population as a whole (compared to random sampling). However, as a result the sample may be biased because all members (or areas) do not have an equal chance of being selected.

2.5.3 Stratified sampling

In stratified sampling, the population is divided into categories that are then sampled proportionally. This means the population is organised into groups or "strata" according to some characteristic (e.g. age) and the number of individuals sampled from each group is in proportion to the group's size in the main population. In an environmental study this may mean an area is split into separate habitats and proportionally sampled.

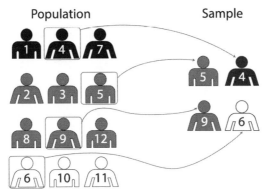

Stratified sampling

The main advantage of stratified sampling is that it should give a sample which is highly representative of the population as a whole. The difficulty with the use of stratified sampling is that the proportions of each group within the main population must be known. In order to identify the relative proportion of each group, the researcher must have access to accurate, up-to-date population data and this is not always available.

2.6 Ensuring reliability

Before investigating how we can ensure reliability in a scientific investigation we must understand the terms precision, accuracy, validity and reliability.

Term	Definition	Explanation
Precision	The closeness of repeated measurements to one another.	Precise results are obtained when the data has very little spread about the mean value.
Accuracy	A measure of how close the data is to the actual true value.	Accuracy of measuring equipment can be improved by performing a calibration with a known standard. This can improve the accuracy of the data which is collected.
Validity	Refers to whether conclusions drawn from a set of results are credible. Valid results rely on sound experimental design and execution.	Results are considered valid if all confounding variables have been controlled; therefore, only the independent variable affected the dependent variable.
Reliability	Refers to whether a procedure yields consistent results each time it is repeated.	Carrying out repeat measurements within an investigation can improve the reliability of the results. A result is considered reliable if it can be re-produced both by the initial researcher and other scientists.

Precision and accuracy can be difficult to distinguish between. Look at the diagram below, imagine the "true value" is the centre circle: (a) is neither precise nor accurate, (b) is precise and accurate and (c) is precise but inaccurate.

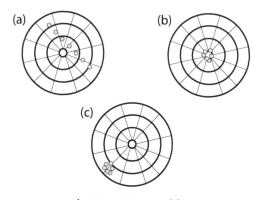

Accuracy versus precision

When variation arises in experimental results, this may be due to the reliability of measurement methods. To determine the reliability of measuring instruments being used in an investigation, a researcher can take repeated measurements or readings of an individual datum point. The variation observed in the results indicates the precision of the measurement instrument or procedure but not necessarily its accuracy.

For example, in an experiment using a colorimeter to take an absorbance reading of a solution a researcher may take three absorbance readings of a solution and find that the readings are all very similar. This indicates that the results are precise because there is little variation around the mean value. The results, however, could still be inaccurate. For example if the cuvette being used to hold the solution was not clean the absorbance readings would be affected and the results would be inaccurate.

Variation in experimental results may also be due to the inherent variation in the specimens. The natural variation in the biological material being used can be determined by measuring a sample of individuals from the population. The mean of these repeated measurements will give an indication of the true value being measured. Using a larger sample size should help to produce a more representative result by showing the full range of data present within the population. Using the data from a large sample group should then provide the most accurate mean value for the characteristic being studied.

For example in an investigation into the effect of population density on average shell length of limpets, researchers may find large variation in their repeat measurements.

Limpets
(Common limpets (http://bit.ly/1NDmVg4) by Tango22 (http://bit.ly/1QOZwsl) is licensed under CC BY-SA 3.0 (http://bit.ly/1kvyKWi))

This variation may arise due to the reliability of measurement methods, i.e. measuring limpet shell length using a ruler with mm subdivisions may not provide an accurate result. It may also be difficult to accurately measure the shell length due to its uneven shape. Genetic differences between limpets may result in added variation in shell length data, thus increasing variation within the results even further. Altogether the variation due to measurement methods and the inherent variation within the population will reduce the reliability of the results. Increasing the sample size would provide the most representative results and allow a more accurate mean to be calculated.

Reliability of results is something which all research scientists strive to achieve. Results are considered to be reliable when they can be achieved consistently both by the initial researcher and other scientists following the same procedure. The main reason behind the need for reliability is that in order for results to be considered to be significant, they must be repeatable, not just a one off result. By ensuring results are both reliable and valid, findings are likely to be accepted as true by the scientific community.

2.7 Extended response

Q7: Discuss the advantages of building a pilot study into the development of a biological investigation. *(4 marks)*

. . . .

2.8 Learning points

Summary

- A pilot study is a small-scale investigation of a planned research project.

- A pilot study is used to help plan procedures, assess validity and check techniques; this allows evaluation and modification of experimental design.

- Pilot studies allow development of a new protocol as well as enabling the investigator to become proficient in using an established protocol.

- The use of a pilot study can ensure an appropriate range of values for the independent variable to avoid results for the dependent variable ending up 'off the scale'.

- A pilot study can be used to check whether results can be produced in a suitable time frame.

- Pilot studies allow the number of repeat measurements required to be estimated as well as identification of confounding variables which can then be controlled.

- The independent variable is the variable that is changed or controlled in a scientific experiment to test the effects on the dependent variable.

- The dependent variable is the variable being tested and measured in a scientific experiment.

- A confounding variable is any factor which affects the dependent variable that is not the independent variable.

- These confounding variables must be held constant if possible, or at least monitored so that their effect on the results can be accounted for in the analysis.

- In cases where confounding variables cannot easily be controlled, blocks of experimental and control groups can be distributed in such a way that the influence of any confounding variable is likely to be the same across the experimental and control groups.

- Variables can be discrete or continuous and give rise to qualitative, quantitative or ranked data.

- The type of variable being investigated has consequences for any graphical display or statistical tests that may be used.

- Experiments involve the manipulation of the independent variable by the investigator.

- The experimental treatment group is compared to a control.

- Simple experiments involve a single independent variable.

Summary continued

- A multifactorial experiment involves a combination of more than one independent variable or combination of treatments.

- The control of laboratory conditions allows simple experiments to be conducted more easily than in the field.

- Experiments conducted in vivo tend to be more complex than those in vitro.

- A drawback of a simple experiment is that its findings may not be applicable to a wider setting.

- In some studies the investigator may wish to use groups that already exist, so there is no truly independent variable. These 'observational' studies are good at detecting correlation but, as they do not directly test the model, they are less useful for determining causation.

- The results of control groups are used for comparison with treatment results.

- The negative control group provides results in the absence of a treatment.

- A positive control is a treatment that is included to check that the system can detect a positive result when it occurs.

- Where it is impractical to measure every individual, a representative sample of the population is selected.

- The extent of the natural variation within a population determines the appropriate sample size. More variable populations require a larger sample size.

- A representative sample should share the same mean and the same degree of variation about the mean as the population as a whole.

- In random sampling, members of the population have an equal chance of being selected.

- In systematic sampling, members of a population are selected at regular intervals.

- In stratified sampling, the population is divided into categories that are then sampled proportionally.

- Variation in experimental results may be due to the reliability of measurement methods and/or inherent variation in the specimens.

- The reliability of measuring instruments or procedures can be determined by repeated measurements or readings of an individual datum point. The variation observed indicates the precision of the measurement instrument or procedure but not necessarily its accuracy.

- The natural variation in the biological material being used can be determined by measuring a sample of individuals from the population. The mean of these repeated measurements will give an indication of the true value being measured.

Summary continued

- Overall results can only be considered reliable if they can be achieved consistently.

- An experiment should be repeated as a whole to check the reliability of the results.

2.9   End of topic test

Go online

End of Topic 2 test

Q8:   Match each of the following terms to its correct definition in the table below: *(4 marks)*

- Accuracy;
- Precision;
- Reliability;
- Validity.

Term	Definition
	The closeness of repeated measurements to one another.
	A measure of how close the data is to the actual true value.
	Refers to whether conclusions drawn from a set of results are credible.
	Refers to whether a procedure yields consistent results each time it is repeated.

....

Q9:   An experiment was conducted to investigate the effect of increasing work rate on oxygen uptake in an adult male. The subject was asked to run on a treadmill at a constant speed. The work rate (measured in watts) was increased periodically by increasing the incline of the treadmill. The results of the experiment are shown below.

Work rate (watts)	Oxygen uptake (cm^3 kg^{-1} min^{-1})
50	10
75	15
100	24
125	31
150	36
175	42
200	45

Which is the dependent variable in the experiment? *(1 mark)*

a) Work rate
b) Oxygen uptake

....

Q10:   An experiment was conducted into habitat selection by the sea slug *Onchidoris bilamellata*. The study investigated the effect of both light intensity and texture of surface on habitat selection. The results showed that the sea slugs preferred rough surfaces rather than smooth, however, their surface preference was always overridden by their preference for darkness over light.

What name is given to an experiment, such as this, which has more than one independent variable? *(1 mark)*

....

Q11: Male magnificent frigatebirds (*Fregata magnificens*) have a large red pouch on their throats which they use to make a thrumming sound to attract a mate.

Researchers conducted a study to determine if pouch size was related to the frequency of sound produced. Results from the study are shown in the scatterplot below.

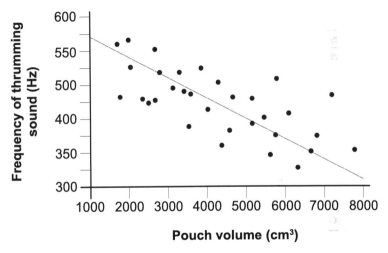

Scatterplot showing the results from the magnificent frigatebird study

Explain why the results are thought to have low reliability. *(1 mark)*

....

Q12: A student carried out an investigation into the effect of caffeine on reaction time. She obtained a list of every pupil in her year group and selected every fifth person to take part in the experiment. What type of sampling does this demonstrate? *(1 mark)*

....

An experiment was conducted to investigate the effect of different metal ions on lipase enzyme activity. The effect of magnesium, cobalt, calcium, potassium, copper and zinc ions was investigated. The enzyme was extracted and purified from a bacterium called *P. aeruginosa*. The enzyme solution was mixed with 1mM of the various ions (as chloride salts) or distilled water (to act as a control) and incubated in a water bath at 30°C for one hour. After the allotted time, the enzyme activity was measured and calculated relative to control activity.

The results of the experiment are shown in the table below.

Metal ion	Enzyme activity (% of control)
Control	100
Magnesium	136
Cobalt	89
Calcium	81
Potassium	79
Copper	73
Zinc	68

Q13: Complete the sentences below, choosing the correct option from the two available options in brackets. *(5 marks)*

This experiment was conducted (*in vitro/in vivo*) . The (*dependent/independent*) variable (metal ions) is a (*discrete/continuous*) variable, while the (*dependent/independent*) variable (enzyme activity) is a (*discrete/continuous*) variable.

. . . .

Q14: What type of control is described in the information above? *(1 mark)*

. . . .

Q15: Confounding variables, such as temperature, were tightly controlled throughout the experiment. Explain what is meant by the term confounding variable. *(1 mark)*

. . . .

Q16: Describe the results of the experiment. *(1 mark)*

. . . .

Q17: What evidence is there to suggest that the experiment was only performed once for each type of ion? *(1 mark)*

. . . .

. . . .

Topic 3

Critical evaluation of biological research

Contents

3.1 Evaluating background information 45
3.2 Evaluating experimental design 46
3.3 Evaluating data analysis 47
3.4 Evaluating conclusions 51
3.5 Learning points 55
3.6 End of topic test 57

Prerequisite knowledge

You should already know that:

- *an evaluation is an important part of a scientific report that outlines sources of error, validity of procedures and any possible improvements;*

- *reliable and relevant sources are used to support background information;*

- *results and data can be presented in a variety of ways, most commonly as graphs and tables;*

- *simple calculations such as averages can be used when interpreting data;*

- *conclusions should refer back to the aim of the investigation.*

Learning objectives

By the end of this topic you should be able to:

- *state that all scientific reports require:*
    - *an informative title;*
    - *abstract or summary - aims and findings;*
    - *introduction which contains enough detail and context to allow the reader to understand the rest of the report;*

- *explain that references and citations should be used to support statements made in the report, and describe the standard format used for citing and referencing;*

- explain that a method should be present and detailed enough to allow another scientist to repeat the experiment;

- explain that it is important for the procedure to test the aim or hypothesis;

- state that key variables need to be controlled throughout the experiment in order to allow valid conclusions to be made;

- explain that the sample should be random, where possible and appropriate, and of suitable size to allow an unbiased conclusion to be drawn that the independent variable had an effect;

- describe means by which data may be presented, including graphs and tables;

- explain that calculating the mean, median, mode, standard deviation or range of data, where appropriate, can be useful in the interpretation of data;

- state that care must be taken when interpreting results from one-off data or any data that fails to follow the trend;

- describe what error bars and confidence intervals are;

- state that error bars drawn on graphs and the use of confidence intervals can be used to show whether the effect caused by the changing the independent variable may be considered as significant or not;

- state that a correlation does not always imply causation;

- state that the conclusion(s) should refer back to the original aim and hypothesis;

- explain that the suitability, accuracy, validity and reliability of the procedures used in the experiment must be evaluated;

- state that only when the procedure has been deemed valid and results considered significant, can a valid conclusion be drawn;

- explain that conclusions must also be backed up with findings from other reliable investigations that have also been peer reviewed and determined to be valid.

3.1 Evaluating background information

Scientific reports follow this standard format:

1. Title - this should be descriptive and helpful.

2. **Summary** or abstract - short paragraph outlining the aims and findings.

3. Introduction - a concise account providing clear, relevant and unambiguous background information of a suitable depth and detail, whilst justifying the purpose of the study.

4. Methods - clear and detailed to allow easy repetition by a peer.

5. Results - these should be laid out in an appropriate format, e.g. tables with graphs.

6. Discussion - both procedures and results should be evaluated here, allowing valid conclusions to be formed.

The introduction should:

- provide the reader with sufficient information to understand specific aspects of the methods, results and ultimately the discussion;

- provide convincing justification for the study;

- place the study in the context of what is already known and understood about the topic;

- review any key points which both support and contradict the information provided;

- contain several sources to support statements, and citations and references should be in a standard form;

- give details about the ethical considerations behind the decisions made when selecting the particular study methods and organisms;

- contain clear aims and hypotheses.

Evaluating background information

Q1: Give two requirements of the summary.

....

Go online

Q2: In the introduction, what should the writer include to support statements?

....

Q3: A scientist is using *Drosophila melanogaster* in an experiment. What comments regarding this organism should they give in their introduction?

....

3.2 Evaluating experimental design

In order to make a conclusion, the experiment procedure must be evaluated and deemed to be valid and reliable. The following should be considered:

- **procedures** - these should test the aim or hypothesis;

- **controls** - should be present where appropriate in order to determine that any effects are the result of the treatment or show the effect in the absence of a treatment;

- **controlled variables** - the validity of an experiment may be compromised where factors other than the independent variable may have influenced the dependent variable. A good example of this is ensuring pH remains constant using buffers and temperature remains constant using a water bath;

- **sample size** - must be large enough to state without bias that any effect on the dependent variable was due to changing the independent variable. Of course we know from earlier in this unit that in some experiments there may be no effect, and that a negative result can be just as valid. When taking a sample this must be done randomly to ensure that the sample is representative of the entire population, thus preventing **selection bias**;

- **repetition** - experiments must then be repeated in full at a different time using new ingredients to determine reliability.

Evaluating experimental design

Go online

Q4: Put the following terms into the correct row in the table below:

- Controlled variables;
- Controls;
- Repetition;
- Sample size;
- Selection bias.

Term	Definition
	Experiment set up to show that any effects are the result of the treatment
	Variables that may influence the dependent variable should remain constant throughout the experiment
	Large enough to allow a valid conclusion that the independent variable did have an effect on the dependent variable
	Carrying out the experiment again at a different time with new ingredients to determine reliability
	Where individuals, groups or data are not selected randomly, therefore failing to provide a representative sample

. . . .

3.3   Evaluating data analysis

In results, data should be presented in a clear, concise and logical manner that permits analysis. This will often be in the form of a graph supported by a table. Raw data should be present in an appendix.

Quantitative or qualitative?

Most experiments involve measuring variables and will therefore be based on **quantitative data** (numbers). Some experiments, however, involve making judgements based on observations.   The data in this case will be descriptive and is termed **qualitative**.

Statistics

Data can be further analysed through the appropriate use of simple statistical procedures including:

- **graphs** - should be appropriate type with suitable scales, labels and be plotted accurately. These can be computer generated, however, sometimes the computer program does not produce these to the standard required and drawing by hand is often more suitable. Where possible, **error bars** (95% **confidence intervals**) should be included.

- **mean** - this is the arithmetical average. Add all the values and divide by the number there are.

- **median** - this is the middle point from the range of values. In some cases it may be the same or similar to the mean. If the data is skewed the median may be quite different from the mean.

- **mode** - this is the most common value in a set of data.

- **range** - this is the set of values that the data falls into, thus the smallest value to the biggest value and everything in between, e.g. in an experiment where the wing spans of garden birds were measured the range is the smallest wing span to the largest wing span and all wing spans between.

- **standard deviation (SD)** - shows how much variation or spread from the average/mean exists. The lower the standard deviation the closer the data points are to the mean. Where the standard deviation is higher, this means that the data is spread over a much larger range of values.

Working out the standard deviation is particularly useful when comparing two or more sets of data with the same mean but different ranges. For example, the mean of the following two sets of data is the same: 15, 15, 15, 14, 16 and 2, 7, 14, 22, 30. However, the second is clearly more spread out, thus has a greater range.

Where data is inconsistent and irregular, or where there is a large range and high standard deviation, the validity of the results may be called into question. There are a range of statistical tests that can be used to assess how likely results are to have occurred by chance or if they are in fact significantly different.

Confidence intervals or error bars are indicated in tables or on graphs, showing the spread of data around a mean. Usually, a valid conclusion can be drawn where the average value in the control experiments is significantly different from the average when a treatment has been applied. If the error bars in the treatment experiment overlap with the error bars in the control experiment, it is not usually possible to state with confidence that the treatment has had an effect.

The following data is completely fictional, and has been produced to allow candidates to develop skills in analysing data. The table below shows results for an experiment into the effect of different fertilisers on tomato plant yield.

Fertiliser	Crop yield (kg per hectare)	Standard error with 95% confidence intervals
Supermarket own brand	120	±3.9
Sheep manure	300	±9.4
Chicken manure	180	±4.5
Seaweed extract	340	±10
Tremendous tomatoes	400	±12.7

The graph below shows how these results appear in a graph including error bars.

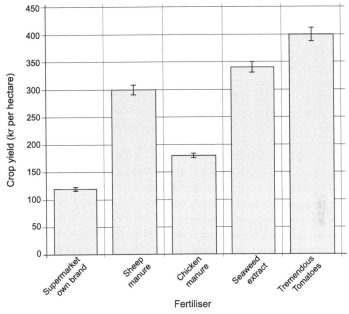

Fertiliser

Graph showing tomato plant yield

As can be seen from the graph above, a valid conclusion can be drawn that tomato plants treated with tremendous tomatoes fertiliser had the greatest yield since error bars do not overlap, and the error bars are not too big.

T-test

The t-test is another statistical test that is useful in determining whether two sets of data are significantly different enough to make a valid conclusion that the treatment has had an effect. The test produces a p-value. Generally if this value is less than 0.05 the null hypothesis can be rejected, thus the treatment has had an effect.

Evaluating data analysis

Q5: Put the following statistical terms into the correct row in the table below:

Go online

- Error bar;
- Mean;
- Mode;
- Qualitative;
- Quantitative;
- Range;
- Standard deviation.

Statistical term	Definition
	Data that is measured
	Data that is observed
	The spread or variation of data from the mean
	Average
	Most common value in a set of data
	Full set of data values
	Line drawn on a graph to show the spread of data around the mean

. . . .

Go online

Dog foods experiment

The following data is completely fictional, and has been produced to allow candidates to develop skills in analysing data. The table below shows the results obtained from an experiment investigating the effect of different dog foods on puppy growth.

Dog food	Increase in mass (kg)	Standard error with 95% confidence intervals
Supermarket own brand	2.2	±0.3
Woof Woof	3.6	±0.2
Bark and be Happy	1.8	±0.1
Wags a lot	4.2	±0.2
Puppy Power	5.6	±0.4

Q6: Present the data in the table as a graph with error bars.

. . . .

Q7: Draw a valid conclusion from the data in table or from your graph.

. . . .

Q8: What about the data allows you able to make this valid conclusion?

. . . .

Nine husky puppies were in each group. Below is the raw data for Puppy Power and Bark and be Happy.

		Increase In mass for each husky(kg)								
	1	2	3	4	5	6	7	8	9	10
Puppy Power	5.2	6.3	6.4	5.5	5.5	5.4	5.2	5.5	5.6	5.6
Bark and be Happy	1.1	3.4	0.9	1.8	1.2	4.0	0.6	1.1	2.1	2.0

Q9: For which dog food out of Puppy Power and Bark and be Happy, in the table above, is the standard deviation the greatest?

. . . .

Q10: The set of results for which of these two dog foods would provide a conclusion where validity could be questioned and why?

. . . .

. . . .

3.4 Evaluating conclusions

In evaluating conclusions, reference should be made to:

- the aim of the study;
- the results obtained;
- the validity and reliability of the experimental design.

Any conclusion should refer back to a hypothesis, stating whether it should be rejected or not. Consideration should be given as to whether significant results can be attributed to **correlation** or **causation**.

Meaningful scientific discussion would include consideration of findings in the context of existing knowledge and the results of other investigations, thus backed by scientific reading. Scientific writing should reveal an awareness of the contribution of scientific research to increasing scientific knowledge and to the social, economic and industrial life of the community. It is here that any significance of the findings are discussed. Do your findings have a potential impact on society, living things or the environment?

Critical analysis of results is an essential part of any conclusion. This is where you take your statistical evidence to state that the conclusion is valid because SD's are small, p-values are small or there is little variation between repeat experiments. You should discuss that there is a big difference between the control group and the experiment group (if there is), making reference to the error bars or confidence intervals. Generally, if the error bars for the control and treatment groups show no overlap, the data may be considered different, thus supporting valid conclusions.

Correlation or causation?

Correlation is where two variables seem to vary together, thus seem to be connected. For example, there is likely to be a correlation between how many sweets a child eats and their incidence of tooth decay.

A **positive correlation** is when an increase in the independent variable seems connected to the increase in the dependent variable. An example of a positive correlation would be that as the external temperature increases, the volume of sweat produced by an individual also increases.

A **negative correlation** is when the dependent variable decreases as the independent variable is increased. An example of a negative correlation would be that as a dairy cow gets older, the volume of milk it produces falls.

A correlation, however, does not always prove that changing the independent variable has directly caused the change in the dependent variable. In short, correlation does not always indicate causation.

Example

A correlation has been found that individuals in some families are more likely to be obese than individuals from other families. This has resulted in some theories surrounding presence of an 'obese gene', thus implying that a gene is causing obesity. Care must be taken when making such a statement.

Obesity is also linked to diet and lifestyle. It is probable that individuals in the same family eat similar foods and follow similar lifestyles. If parents eat a balanced diet and lead active lifestyles, so too do their children. Similarly, where parents eat diets high in saturated fat and sugars, and follow a less active lifestyle, their children often mirror this.

It is therefore, impossible without further study to determine that obesity is caused by a gene, despite there being a clear link between family and obesity.

Go online

Positive and negative correlations

Q11: As chickens get older, the number of eggs laid falls.

a) Positive correlation
b) Negative correlation

....

Q12: As the mass of nitrate increases, the greater the dry mass of algae.

a) Positive correlation
b) Negative correlation

. . . .

Q13: As the level of dissolved oxygen in the river increases so too does the population density of mayfly nymphs.

a) Positive correlation
b) Negative correlation

. . . .

Q14: The longer a person participates in ballet, the larger the surface area of their cerebellum becomes.

a) Positive correlation
b) Negative correlation

. . . .

Q15: The more an athlete trains, the lower their resting pulse rate becomes.

a) Positive correlation
b) Negative correlation

. . . .

Q16: The vitamin C content of broccoli falls as the length of boiling time increases.

a) Positive correlation
b) Negative correlation

. . . .

The graph below displays results of an experiment to investigate how milk production in cows changes as cows age.

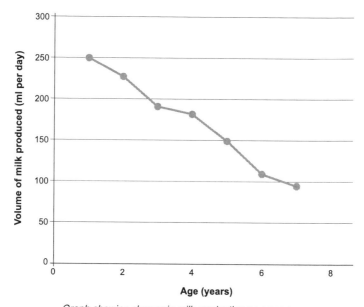

Graph showing change in milk production as cows age

Q17: Is there a correlation between the two variables? If so, is the correlation positive or negative? Give a reason for your answer.

3.5 Learning points

Summary

- All scientific reports should start with an informative title.

- An abstract or summary should follow the title. This states the aims and findings.

- An introduction should follow, providing some background information, enough details to allow the reader to understand the report and an explanation of the context within which the study is set.

- The information in the introduction should be supported by several relevant and reliable sources, correctly cited and referenced.

- The introduction should be followed by the methods section, which should provide clear details which will allow a fellow scientist to repeat the investigation.

- The method should test the aims and hypotheses which should be clearly stated.

- The method should also clearly describe how the independent variable will be changed, how the dependent variable will be measured and how the controlled variables will remain unchanged to maintain validity.

- Within the method, the sample size should be stated, and the manner in which the sample is selected be described.

- A large and unbiased sample group is essential to ensure representative sampling and allow the investigator to show that altering the independent variable has in fact had an effect on the dependent variable.

- A results section will follow the method. This is where data is presented in an appropriate and concise manner.

- Data is usually presented as tables and graphs, with statistical analysis used as appropriate.

- A mean can be calculated from raw data.

- Other statistics such as median, mode and range may also be used.

- Standard deviation can be used to assess the spread of data.

- Scientists should be wary of one-off results or anomalous data.

- Statistical tests such as t-test may be used to determine whether a result is significant or merely due to chance.

- Confidence intervals or error bars can be included in tables or on graphs and show how the data varies from the mean.

Summary continued

- Where the treatment results differ significantly from the control group so that there is no overlap between confidence intervals, the two sets of data can be concluded to be different.

- Conclusions should refer back to the original aim and hypothesis.

- For conclusions to be valid, the method must be evaluated in terms validity and reliability. This may include discussing controlled variables, sample size, repetition and accuracy of measurements.

- Conclusions may also be explained or supported through referencing to other studies, again using correct citing and referencing styles.

- Within the conclusion, the economic, social or environmental impact of the findings should be discussed.

- Care should be taken when making conclusions as a correlation between two variables does not always mean that altering one variable has caused the effect on the other.

3.6   End of topic test

End of Topic 3 test

Go online

Q18: A Biology pupil writes the following summary: "The results showed that the seaweed Channel Wrack is found mostly at the top of the shore whereas Dabberlocks is found in the lower shore."

What has the pupil missed out in their summary? *(1 mark)*

....

Q19: Which of the following statements about the scientific method are true? *(3 marks)*

a) It only needs to be a brief outline of the experiment.

b) It should provide sufficient detail to allow repetition by other scientists.

c) It should test the aims and hypotheses.

d) It gives details of variables that should be controlled throughout.

....

Q20: Give four statistical procedures that could be used to analyse data. *(4 marks)*

....

Q21: Complete the sentence below, choosing the correct option from the two available options in brackets. *(3 marks)*

Sample size should be *(large/small)* and selected *(randomly/specifically)* to *(avoid/ensure)* selection bias.

....

Q22: Select the positive correlations from the list below. *(2 marks)*

a) As height increases, the number of spines on holly leaves decreases.

b) As temperature increases, mass of seaweed decreases.

c) As tail length increases, mating success in peacocks increases.

d) As length of time as a gymnast increases, surface area of the cerebellum increases.

....

Q23: In order to reach a valid conclusion, procedures must be .... *(1 mark)*

....

Topic 4

End of unit test

Contents

4.1 End of Unit 3 test 60

4.1   End of Unit 3 test

End of Unit 3 test

Go online

The following experiment and data is fictional. The cited sources are also fictional, added in merely to allow the outcomes to be assessed.

Summary

The main findings of this investigation were that regular medium intensity of exercise for five hours a week significantly lowered resting pulse rate compared to those who did not exercise regularly. More intense or longer duration of exercise showed no further benefit to lowering resting pulse rate.

Background information

The heart is a muscular pump responsible for pumping blood around the body and to the lungs, each time it beats. A healthy resting pulse rate is said to be between 60-80bpm. It has been suggested that a lower resting pulse rate indicates that the heart muscle is stronger and capable of pumping a greater volume of blood with each beat. The heart is therefore under less strain. Pulse can be felt in arteries close to the surface of the skin each time blood is forced from the heart. It has long been reported that participating in regular activity can be a major factor in lowering resting pulse rate (Wilson, 2014), however, the intensity and duration of the exercise required is still unclear in many reports.

This experiment compared and analysed resting pulse rate data from a control group of 30 individuals who did not take regular exercise, with two treatment groups, each of 30 individuals. Treatment group one regularly participated in five hours of moderate intensity exercise per week. Treatment group two regularly participated in eight hours of high intensity exercise per week. In a second experiment, a different 20 individuals who had never participated in regular exercise agreed to exercise for three hours a week for 10 weeks. Their resting pulse rate was measured before and after.

Q1:   The aim has been left out of the summary. Which of the following would be a suitable aim for this experiment? *(1 mark)*

a)   To find out the effect of regular exercise on fitness.
b)   To find out the effect of exercise intensity and duration on resting pulse rate.
c)   To find out the effect of exercise intensity and duration on mass of heart muscle.

....

Q2:   Which of the following provides a suitable null hypothesis for this experiment? *(1 mark)*

a)   The greater the level of activity the higher the resting pulse rate.
b)   Those who participate in regular activity will have healthier hearts.
c)   Exercise intensity and duration will have no effect on resting pulse rate.

....

Q3:   This experiment involves working with human subjects over the age of 16.

Which of the following statements are true regarding the need for informed consent? *(3 marks)*

a) Ensures participants know they can withdraw at any time.
b) Ensures participants know that once they sign up they have to complete the study.
c) Allows participants to assess any harm or risk that might be associated with the experiment.
d) Allows participants to assess any benefits to society that may arise from the results of the investigation.
e) Only those over the age of 16 are eligible for informed consent.

. . . .

Q4: In the background information, how did the writer support the idea that regular exercise lowers resting pulse rate? *(1 mark)*

. . . .

Method

Subjects

The subjects included in the experiment were volunteers aged between 40 and 55 years. All participants received a health check before taking part in the experiment and came from a similar socio-economic background. Each experimental group comprised an even balance of 50% males and 50% females with an average age of 47 ± 1. Age range did not differ between the control and treatment groups.

Experiment 1

In experiment 1, 30 individuals were included in a control group which did not take part in regular exercise. For treatment group 1, 30 individuals were asked to follow an exercise regime which involved five hours of moderate intensity exercise per week. Moderate intensity exercise included fast-paced walking, water aerobics, hiking and gentle bike riding. For treatment group 2, 30 individuals were asked to follow an exercise regime which involved eight hours of high intensity exercise per week. High intensity exercise included jogging/running, fast-paced swimming, aerobics and singles tennis. After 12 weeks, the resting pulse rate of each participant was taken using a digital pulse rate monitor.

Experiment 2

In experiment 2, 20 individuals who had never participated in regular exercise were asked to follow an exercise regime which involved three hours of moderate intensity exercise per week. Moderate intensity exercise included fast-paced walking, water aerobics, hiking and gentle bike riding. The resting pulse rate of each participant was taken using a digital pulse rate monitor before beginning the exercise regime and again 10 weeks later.

Q5: Which of the following best describes the independent variable in experiment 1? *(1 mark)*

a) Age and gender of the participants
b) Whether participants participated in regular exercise or not
c) Pulse rate of participants

. . . .

Q6: Describe the ethical considerations carried out in this investigation. *(1 mark)*

....

Q7: The researcher identified age as a confounding variable. How did they try to ensure the influence of this confounding variable was the same across the experimental and control groups? *(1 mark)*

....

Q8: Experiment 1 investigated both duration and intensity of exercise. What term describes an experiment like this which involves a combination of treatments? *(1 mark)*

....

Q9: In experiment 1, the individuals in the control group did not take regular exercise. Explain how this group acts as a negative control. *(1 mark)*

....

Q10: This research is an example of a field study where the experiments were conducted outwith the laboratory environment. Give a disadvantage of conducting the experiment in this way. *(1 mark)*

....

Q11: In both experiments, the researcher used a digital pulse rate monitor to measure the pulse rate of each participant. How could the reliability of the digital pulse rate monitor be determined? *(1 mark)*

....

Results for experiment 1

The results in the table are mean values of the resting pulse rates of the 30 individuals in each of the three groups, with 95% confidence intervals included.

Group	Mean resting pulse rate (bpm)
Control	98 ± 8
Treatment 1 - moderate intensity exercise for five hours per week	61 ± 3
Treatment 2 - high intensity exercise for eight hours per week	55 ± 14

Q12: What sort of data is present in the table above? *(1 mark)*

....

Q13: Following statistical analysis of the data in the above table, the following statements were made:

- Individuals who participated in moderate intensity exercise for five hours a week had significantly lower resting pulse rates compared to the control group;

- Individuals who participated in high intensity exercise for eight hours a week did not have significantly lower resting pulse rates compared to treatment group 1.

What evidence from the table supports these statements? *(1 mark)*

....

Q14: What type of relationship exists between participation in regular exercise and resting pulse rate? *(1 mark)*

....

Results for experiment 2

The results in the table are mean values of the resting pulse rates of the 20 individuals before and after their exercise programme.

Time	Mean resting pulse rate (bpm)
Before	101 ± 6
After	74 ± 4

Q15: Calculate the percentage decrease (to one decimal place) in resting pulse after participating in the exercise programme. *(1 mark)*

....

Q16: In the discussion the investigator writes: *"All individuals in the study were volunteers from a small church group aged 40-55 years old."*

What might a peer be worried about when reading this statement during peer review? *(1 mark)*

....

Citric acid is used as a flavouring agent and is produced commercially using the mold *Aspergillus niger (A. niger)*. Previous experiments have confirmed that *A. niger* is capable of utilising sucrose to produce citric acid, however, little research has been conducted into the utilisation of other sugars. An experiment was therefore conducted to investigate the effect of different types of sugar (glucose, fructose, lactose or galactose) on citric acid production.

Cultures of *A. niger* were grown in a fermenter with growth medium containing either glucose, fructose, lactose or galactose. After 14 days, the citric acid and sugar content of each sample was determined using liquid chromatography. The results are shown in the table below.

Sugar	Sugar utilised (g/l) [a]	Citric acid (g/l)	Citric acid yield (%) [b]
Glucose	88	34	38
Fructose	75	22	29
Lactose	66	7	11
Galactose	70	0	0

[a] Initial sugar concentration 140 g/l
[b] Based on sugar utilised

Q17: Identify the independent variable in this experiment. *(1 mark)*

....

Q18: Use the information above to design a positive control for this experiment. *(1 mark)*

....

Q19: The researchers monitored but did not control the pH in the fermentation vessel because previous experiments have shown that pH is not a confounding variable. Explain what is meant by the term confounding variable. *(1 mark)*

....

Q20: In this investigation, what would be a suitable null hypothesis? *(1 mark)*

....

Q21: Describe the results of the experiment. *(1 mark)*

....

Q22: Explain why the results of this investigation may not be reliable. *(1 mark)*

....

An experiment was conducted to investigate the effect of caffeine on reaction time. Prior to embarking on the main study, a small scale investigation was conducted and found that the two treatment groups should be administered 500 mg or 250 mg of caffeine.

For the main study, thirty female students aged between 18 and 22 were systematically sampled from a university population (the process was repeated to select thirty male participants). Ten women and ten men were randomly assigned to one of three groups. The experiment was conducted in a double-blind manner. Participants from treatment group 1 were administered 500 mg caffeine, treatment group 2 were administered 250 mg of caffeine and group 3 (the control group) were given a placebo. Reaction time was measured using an electronic test before and after consumption of one of the three solutions. The second reaction time test was conducted one hour after consumption of one of the solutions to allow absorption of the caffeine.

Q23: What term describes an experiment, like the one described in the information above, which allows refinement of experimental design before embarking on the main investigation? *(1 mark)*

....

Q24: Describe the process of systematic sampling. *(1 mark)*

....

Q25: This experiment was conducted in a double-blind manner, meaning both the researchers and the subjects are unaware of which treatment is being administered to each group. Suggest how this feature of the study improves its validity. *(1 mark)*

....

Q26: Identify one confounding variable, not already mentioned, which could affect this experiment. *(1 mark)*

....

Q27: Draw two conclusions from the results of the caffeine reaction time study shown in the graph below. *(2 marks)*

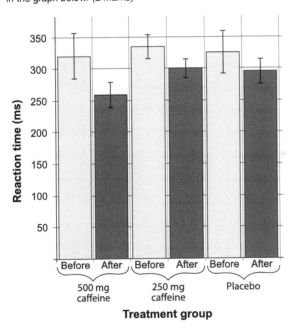

....

Q28: Why would increasing the sample size improve the validity of the conclusions? *(1 mark)*

....

....

Glossary

Causation

> when changing the independent variable causes the effect noted in the dependent variable

Confidence intervals

> a range within which the actual value should lie

Correlation

> when two variables seem to be connected

Error bars

> drawn on graphs to show the spread of data around the mean

Mean

> this is the arithmetical average. Add all the values and divide by the number there are

Median

> this is the middle point from the range of values

Mode

> this is the most common value in a set of data

Negative correlation

> as one variable is increased, the other variable decreases

Parasite load

> a measure of the number of parasite found within a host organism

Placebo

> a substance which has no therapeutic effect

Plagiarism

> copying another person's work or views and passing these off as one's own

Plankton

> microscopic organisms found living in fresh or salt water

Positive correlation

> as one variable increases, the connected variable increases too

Qualitative data

> information that is observed and presented as a description

Quantitative data

> information that can be measured and is usually presented as a number

Range

this is the set of values that the data falls into, thus the smallest value to the biggest value and everything in between

Selection bias

where individuals, groups or data are not selected randomly, therefore failing to provide a representative sample

Standard deviation (SD)

shows how much variation or spread from the average/mean exists

Summary

at the start of the report, where the main aims and findings are described briefly

Answers to questions and activities

1 Scientific principles and process

Scientific cycle (page 5)

Q1:

1. Debating ideas and coming up a hypothesis to test
2. Researching others' work
3. Designing appropriate experiments
4. Observing and collecting data from experiments
5. Analysing data through comparing, interpreting and applying statistics
6. Evaluating results
7. Forming conclusions
8. Refining the original hypothesis

An investigation into whether athletes' body clocks affect competition performance (page 6)

Q2: To find out if athletes' body clocks affected competition performance.

Q3: Athletes' body clocks have no effect on competition performance.

Q4: *Competitors* - they will know that the timing of the event will not affect their performance.

Coaches - they don't need to worry about putting together different teams for different competition times.

Event holders - they won't be accused of being unfair due to the timing of their event.

Scientific ethics (page 9)

Q5:

Term	Definition
Refine	Ensuring competence in the experimental technique to reduce human error.
Replace	Using a different type of animal in the study.
Reduce	Using fewer animals in the study.

An investigation into whether athletes' body clocks affect competition performance (page 10)

Q6: Subject consent and subjects aware of the right to withdraw participation or data at any time.

Q7: With reference to another author, cited in the standard format (Parker et al, 2009).

End of Topic 1 test (page 12)

Q8: Null hypothesis

Q9: Peer review

Q10: a) Results can be negative, b) Results can be positive, d) Results will be verified independently and f) Results may cause a hypothesis to be rejected.

Q11: Scientific reports should be written in a manner that allows other scientists to *repeat* (*reproduce*) the experiment for verification or further work.

Q12: a) can reduce bias and b) has a standard format.

Q13: b) Reduce, replace and refine

Q14: c) Consent is required for all and d) Subjects can withdraw data at any time.

2 Experimentation

Controlled experiment 1 (page 29)

Q1: a) Positive

Q2: b) Negative

Controlled experiment 2 (page 29)

Q3: b) Negative

Q4: a) Positive

Controlled experiment 3 (page 29)

Q5: b) Negative

Q6: a) Positive

Answers from page 36.

Q7: Advantages of a pilot study include that it:

1. can be used to develop a new protocol;
2. allows practice of established protocol;
3. ensures appropriate range of values for independent variable;
4. avoids results for dependent variable going "off the scale";
5. allows the number of repeat measurements required to be estimated;
6. checks whether results can be produced in suitable time frame;
7. allows identification of confounding variables (which can then be controlled).

End of Topic 2 test (page 40)

Q8:

Term	Definition
Precision	The closeness of repeated measurements to one another.
Accuracy	A measure of how close the data is to the actual true value.
Validity	Refers to whether conclusions drawn from a set of results are credible.
Reliability	Refers to whether a procedure yields consistent results each time it is repeated.

Q9: b) Oxygen uptake

Q10: Multifactorial

Q11: Possible answers:

- some samples are a long way from best-fit line;
- there are small/no samples for some pouch volumes;
- there are some obvious discrepancies/inconsistencies, i.e.   a wide range of frequencies at the same pouch volume.

Q12: Systematic sampling

Q13: This experiment was conducted *in vitro*. The *independent* variable (metal ions) is a *discrete* variable, while the *dependent* variable (enzyme activity) is a *continuous* variable.

Q14: Negative control

Q15: Any factor affecting the dependent variable that is not the independent variable.

Q16: Magnesium ions increase enzyme activity (by 36%) and all other metal ions decrease enzyme activity (ranging from 11% to 32% decrease).

Q17: There are no variation, error information or confidence intervals reported.

3 Critical evaluation of biological research

Evaluating background information (page 45)

Q1: Aim(s) and finding(s)

Q2: Relevant sources

Q3: Why this organism was chosen and any ethical considerations.

Evaluating experimental design (page 46)

Q4:

Term	Definition
Controls	Experiment set up to show that any effects are the result of the treatment
Controlled variables	Variables that may influence the dependent variable should remain constant throughout the experiment
Sample size	Large enough to allow a valid conclusion that the independent variable did have an effect on the dependent variable
Repetition	Carrying out the experiment again at a different time with new ingredients to determine reliability
Selection bias	Where individuals, groups or data are not selected randomly, therefore failing to provide a representative sample

Evaluating data analysis (page 49)

Q5:

Statistical term	Definition
Quantitative	Data that is measured
Qualitative	Data that is observed
Standard deviation	The spread or variation of data from the mean
Mean	Average
Mode	Most common value in a set of data
Range	Full set of data values
Error bar	Line drawn on a graph to show the spread of data around the mean

Dog foods experiment (page 50)

Q6:

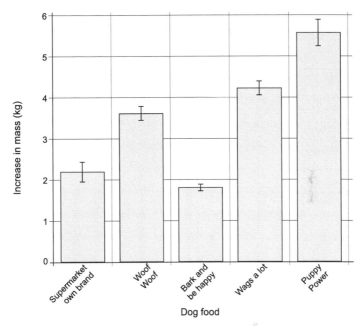

Dog food

Q7: Puppies fed Puppy Power had the greatest increase in body mass, and those fed Bark and be Happy had the least.

Q8: No overlap between error bars / confidence intervals.

Q9: Bark and be Happy

Q10: Bark and be Happy due to the large variation in results, in comparison with Puppy Power where the range in data is much smaller.

Positive and negative correlations (page 52)

Q11: b) Negative correlation

Q12: a) Positive correlation

Q13: a) Positive correlation

Q14: a) Positive correlation

Q15: b) Negative correlation

Q16: b) Negative correlation

Q17: Yes, the two variables are connected.   The correlation is negative; as age increases, milk production decreases.

End of Topic 3 test (page 57)

Q18: Aim

Q19: b) It should provide sufficient detail to allow repetition by other scientists, c) It should test the aims and hypotheses and d) It gives details of variables that should be controlled throughout.

Q20: Any four from:

- mean;
- mode;
- median;
- range;
- standard deviation;
- graphs;
- confidence intervals;
- error bars;
- t-test.

Q21: Sample size should be *large* and selected *randomly* to *avoid* selection bias.

Q22: c) As tail length increases, mating success in peacocks increases and d) As length of time as a gymnast increases, surface area of the cerebellum increases.

Q23: In order to reach a valid conclusion, procedures must be *evaluated*.

4 End of unit test

End of Unit 3 test (page 60)

Q1: b) To find out the effect of exercise intensity and duration on resting pulse rate.

Q2: c) Exercise intensity and duration will have no effect on resting pulse rate.

Q3: a) Ensures participants know they can withdraw at any time, c) Allows participants to assess any harm or risk that might be associated with the experiment and d) Allows participants to assess any benefits to society that may arise from the results of the investigation.

Q4: By using a cited reference (Wilson, 2014).

Q5: b) Whether participants participated in regular exercise or not

Q6: Participants received a health check prior to the investigation.

Q7: By ensuring each group had a similar mean age and age range.

Q8: Multifactorial

Q9: They provide results in the absence of the treatment.

Q10: The researcher cannot be certain that the participants have followed their assigned exercise regime.

Q11: By taking repeated readings of each individual's pulse rate.

Q12: Quantitative

Q13: Either of the following:

- Error bars/95% confidence intervals have a much wider range (±14) in treatment 2 compared to only ±3 in the treatment group.
- Error bars would overlap in treatment 2 when compared to treatment 1, but error bars in treatment one would not overlap with the control.

Q14: Negative correlation

Q15: 26.7%

Q16: Selection bias

Q17: Type of sugar

Q18: Grow *A. niger* with a growth medium containing sucrose.

Q19: A confounding variable is:

- a factor other than the independent variable that may affect dependent variable/results;
- any factor affecting the dependent variable that is not the independent variable.

Q20: The sugars tested will not result in citric acid production.

Q21: Glucose resulted in the highest citric acid production followed by fructose then lactose. No citric acid was produced from galactose.

Q22: There was no independent replication and the whole experiment was only carried out once.

Q23: Pilot study

Q24: Members of a population are selected at regular intervals.

Q25: Either of the following:

- it removes any psychological factors;
- it removes/reduces (researcher) bias.

Q26: Any one of the following:

- weight of participants;
- room temperature;
- type of reaction time test;
- time of day;
- timing of meals;
- time lapse between eating and conducting the test;
- type of food consumed;
- quantity of food consumed;
- liquid refreshments prior to the test;
- anxiety level/emotional factors.

Q27: Any two from the following:

- 500 mg caffeine results in a significant decrease in reaction time;
- 250 mg caffeine does not result in a significant decrease in reaction time;
- the placebo does not result in a significant decrease in reaction time.

Q28: Any one of the following:

- it would give a more representative sample;
- it would better represent the variation in the population;
- it would reduce the impact of uncontrollable confounding variables.